x6 table

Write the answers to the **x6** table here.

1 x 6 =		7 x 6 =
2 x 6 =		8 x 6 =
3 x 6 =		9 x 6 =
4 x 6 =		10 x 6 =
5 x 6 =		11 x 6 =
6 x 6 =		12 x 6 =

Look at this number grid.
Mark all the numbers in the
x6 table with a red **O**.

1	2	3	4	5	6	7	8	9	10
11	12	13	14	15	16	17	18	19	20
21	22	23	24	25	26	27	28	29	30
31	32	33	34	35	36	37	38	39	40
41	42	43	44	45	46	47	48	49	50
51	52	53	54	55	56	57	58	59	60
61	62	63	64	65	66	67	68	69	70
71	72	73	74	75	76	77	78	79	80
81	82	83	84	85	86	87	88	89	90
91	92	93	94	95	96	97	98	99	100

These are the numbers in the **x6** table. They are the **multiples of 6**.

Keep on counting in **6s** up to 100.

Now mark all the **multiples of 3** on the number grid. Use a blue **X**.
Which are the **shared multiples** of 6 and **3**?

_____

Now mark all the **multiples of 2** on the number grid. Use a green **+**.
Which are the **shared multiples** of **6, 3** and **2**?

_____

3

Write the **x6** table here.

☐	x	☐	=	☐
☐	x	☐	=	☐
☐	x	☐	=	☐
☐	x	☐	=	☐
☐	x	☐	=	☐
☐	x	☐	=	☐
☐	x	☐	=	☐
☐	x	☐	=	☐
☐	x	☐	=	☐
☐	x	☐	=	☐
☐	x	☐	=	☐
☐	x	☐	=	☐

Now write it backwards, starting with **12 x 6 =**

☐	x	☐	=	☐
☐	x	☐	=	☐
☐	x	☐	=	☐
☐	x	☐	=	☐
☐	x	☐	=	☐
☐	x	☐	=	☐
☐	x	☐	=	☐
☐	x	☐	=	☐
☐	x	☐	=	☐
☐	x	☐	=	☐
☐	x	☐	=	☐
☐	x	☐	=	☐

Fill in the missing numbers in the **x6** table.

1	x	☐	=	6
☐	x	6	=	☐
3	x	☐	=	☐
☐	x	6	=	24
☐	x	☐	=	☐
6	x	6	=	☐
7	x	6	=	☐
☐	x	6	=	☐
9	x	6	=	☐
☐	x	6	=	☐
11	x	☐	=	66
☐	x	☐	=	72

Time to Travel

You will need: a dice, counters and a friend to play with.

| 1 | 2 | 3 | MISS A GO | 5 | 6 | SAY THE ×5 TABLE | 8 | 9 | GO BACK 1×2 SQUARES | 11 | 12 | 13 |

START HERE   5×5

| | | | | | | | | | | | MOVE ON 6 SQUARES |
| | | | | | | | | | | | 15 |

| 27 | 26 | 25 | MOVE ON 2×6 SQUARES | 23 | 22 | GO BACK 5×1 SQUARES | 20 | TRAP DOOR! STOP UNTIL YOUR NEXT GO... | 18 | 17 | 16 |

MOVE ON 7×2 SQUARES

$7 = ?$ $×2$ $4×4$

| 29 | | | | | | | | | | | |

| 30 | 31 | SAY YOUR ×4 TABLE THEN MOVE ON 4 | 33 | 34 | TRAP DOOR! STOP UNTIL YOUR NEXT GO. | 36 | 37 | MOVE ON 1 SQUARE | 39 | 40 | GO BACK 3 SQUARES |

1866 AD → 1999 AD
1066 AD

| | | | | | | | | | | 42 |
| | | | | | | | | | | 43 |

| 55 | 54 | 53 | 52 | GO BACK 8×3 SQUARES | 50 | 49 | 48 | MOVE ON 3×5 SQUARES | 46 | MISS A GO | 44 |

TRAP DOOR! STOP UNTIL YOUR NEXT GO.

| 57 | 58 | 59 | MISS A GO | 61 | GO BACK 3×1 SQUARES | 63 | MOVE ON 2×4 SQUARES | 65 | 66 | 67 | 68 |

ch player has two throws before it is the
xt player's turn.
row 1: Move on the number of squares
own on the die, e.g. 5 spaces.
row 2: Multiply the first throw by this throw,
g. 5 x 4, and move on that number of squares,
g. 5 x 4 = 20 spaces.
you land on a square with an instruction on
ther throw, you must obey that instruction.
win you must answer the three sums at the end.

$3×5 =$

$5×6 =$

$4×6 =$

| | | TRAP DOOR! STOP UNTIL YOUR NEXT GO... |
| MISS A GO... | 71 | 70 |

Record Breakers

How quickly can you do these tests?
Use a stopwatch and write the answers on spare paper.
Take 1 second off your time for every question you get **right**.
Add 3 seconds onto your time for every question you get **wrong**.

You will score better by being ACCURATE rather than FAST.

BUILD SPEED UP GRADUALLY while still trying to get all the answers right!!

Where you see ? this is the answer you need to give.

Test 1	Test 2	Test 3
? x 6 = 42	2 x ? = 12	? x 6 = 30
5 x 6 = ?	3 x ? = 18	? x 5 = 25
? x 6 = 12	3 x ? = 15	? x 4 = 20
3 x ? = 18	8 x ? = 40	? x 3 = 27
8 x ? = 48	8 x ? = 16	? x 3 = 24
1 x 6 = ?	8 x ? = 48	? x 4 = 28
? x 6 = 36	7 x ? = 35	? x 5 = 20
9 x 6 = ?	9 x ? = 54	? x 6 = 24
? x 6 = 24	5 x ? = 10	? x 6 = 18
? x 6 = 66	9 x ? = 36	? x 10 = 40
12 x 6 = ?	12 x ? = 72	? x 2 = 18
10 x 6 = ?	4 x ? = 24	? x 10 = 70

Keep a record of your times for each test here.

Do one test a day.

Date	Time	Date	Time	Date	Time

6

 **table**

Write the answers to the **x7** table here.

1 x 7 =
2 x 7 =
3 x 7 =
4 x 7 =
5 x 7 =
6 x 7 =
7 x 7 =
8 x 7 =
9 x 7 =
10 x 7 =
11 x 7 =
12 x 7 =

Mark all the answers to the **x7** table on this number square. Use an orange **O**.

1	2	3	4	5	6	7	8	9	10
11	12	13	14	15	16	17	18	19	20
21	22	23	24	25	26	27	28	29	30
31	32	33	34	35	36	37	38	39	40
41	42	43	44	45	46	47	48	49	50
51	52	53	54	55	56	57	58	59	60
61	62	63	64	65	66	67	68	69	70
71	72	73	74	75	76	77	78	79	80
81	82	83	84	85	86	87	88	89	90
91	92	93	94	95	96	97	98	99	100

These are the numbers in the **x7** table. They are the **multiples of 7**.

Count on in **7s** up to 100.

Write the **x7** table here.

☐	x ☐	= ☐
☐	x ☐	= ☐
☐	x ☐	= ☐
☐	x ☐	= ☐
☐	x ☐	= ☐
☐	x ☐	= ☐
☐	x ☐	= ☐
☐	x ☐	= ☐
☐	x ☐	= ☐
☐	x ☐	= ☐
☐	x ☐	= ☐
☐	x ☐	= ☐

Now write it backwards, starting with **12 x 7 =**

☐	x ☐	= ☐
☐	x ☐	= ☐
☐	x ☐	= ☐
☐	x ☐	= ☐
☐	x ☐	= ☐
☐	x ☐	= ☐
☐	x ☐	= ☐
☐	x ☐	= ☐
☐	x ☐	= ☐
☐	x ☐	= ☐
☐	x ☐	= ☐
☐	x ☐	= ☐

Fill in the missing numbers in the **x7** table.

1 x ☐ = 7

☐ x 7 = 14

3 x ☐ = ☐

☐ x 7 = 28

5 x ☐ = 35

☐ x 7 = 42

7 x 7 = ☐

8 x 7 = ☐

☐ x 7 = 63

10 x 7 = ☐

☐ x ☐ = 77

12 x ☐ = ☐

Prehistoric puzzles

Write the missing numbers in these multiplication squares.

X	2	4	6	8	10
7					
6		24			
5				40	

X	3	5	7	9	11
7					
6					66
5	15				

X	6	8	10	9	7
2		16			14
4					
6			60		

X	1	3	9	7	6
1				7	
3		9			
5					

X	2	3	4	5	6
2					
3	6				
4				20	
5					
6					

X	2	3	4	5	6	7
1	2					
8						
9						63
10						
7						
5						

Now travel on to the times tables Record Breakers.

Record Breakers

How quickly can you do these tests?
Use a stopwatch and write the answers on spare paper.
Take 1 second off your time for every question you get **right**.
Add 3 seconds onto your time for every question you get **wrong**.

You will score better by being ACCURATE rather than FAST.

BUILD SPEED UP GRADUALLY while still trying to get all the answers right!!

Where you see ? this is the answer you need to give.

Test 1	Test 2	Test 3
10 x ? = 70	2 x ? = 14	? x 7 = 0
5 x ? = 35	4 x ? = 24	? x 5 = 30
? x 7 = 14	6 x ? = 42	? x 6 = 36
3 x ? = 21	8 x ? = 32	? x 4 = 36
8 x ? = 56	10 x ? = 60	? x 3 = 30
7 x 7 = ?	12 x ? = 72	? x 1 = 9
? x 7 = 42	1 x ? = 7	? x 2 = 4
1 x 7 = ?	3 x ? = 12	? x 10 = 40
? x 7 = 28	5 x ? = 10	? x 5 = 35
9 x ? = 63	7 x ? = 49	? x 6 = 66
? x 7 = 77	9 x ? = 54	? x 7 = 42
12 x 7 = ?	11 x ? = 66	? x 6 = 42

Keep a record of your times for each test here.

Do one test a day

Date	Time	Date	Time	Date	Time

 **table**

Write the answers to the **x8** table here.

1 x 8 = ☐   7 x 8 = ☐

2 x 8 = ☐   8 x 8 = ☐

3 x 8 = ☐   9 x 8 = ☐

4 x 8 = ☐   10 x 8 = ☐

5 x 8 = ☐   11 x 8 = ☐

6 x 8 = ☐   12 x 8 = ☐

Look at this number grid.
Mark all the answers to the
x8 table with a green **O**.

1	2	3	4	5	6	7	8	9	10
11	12	13	14	15	16	17	18	19	20
21	22	23	24	25	26	27	28	29	30
31	32	33	34	35	36	37	38	39	40
41	42	43	44	45	46	47	48	49	50
51	52	53	54	55	56	57	58	59	60
61	62	63	64	65	66	67	68	69	70
71	72	73	74	75	76	77	78	79	80
81	82	83	84	85	86	87	88	89	90
91	92	93	94	95	96	97	98	99	100

These are the numbers in the **x8** table. They are the **multiples of 8**.

Count on in **8s** up to 100.

Now mark all the **multiples of 4** on the number grid with an orange **X**.
Which are the **shared multiples** of **8** and **4**?

_____

Now mark all the **multiples of 2** on the number grid. Use a blue **+**.
Which are the **shared multiples** of **8, 4** and **2**?

_____

Write the **x8** table here.

☐	x	☐	=	☐	
☐	x	☐	=	☐	
☐	x	☐	=	☐	
☐	x	☐	=	☐	
☐	x	☐	=	☐	
☐	x	☐	=	☐	
☐	x	☐	=	☐	
☐	x	☐	=	☐	
☐	x	☐	=	☐	
☐	x	☐	=	☐	
☐	x	☐	=	☐	
☐	x	☐	=	☐	

Now write it backwards, starting with **12 x 8 =**

☐	x	☐	=	☐
☐	x	☐	=	☐
☐	x	☐	=	☐
☐	x	☐	=	☐
☐	x	☐	=	☐
☐	x	☐	=	☐
☐	x	☐	=	☐
☐	x	☐	=	☐
☐	x	☐	=	☐
☐	x	☐	=	☐
☐	x	☐	=	☐
☐	x	☐	=	☐

Fill in the missing numbers in the **x8** table.

1	x	☐	=	8
☐	x	8	=	☐
3	x	☐	=	☐
☐	x	☐	=	32
5	x	☐	=	40
6	x	8	=	☐
7	x	☐	=	56
☐	x	8	=	☐
9	x	8	=	☐
10	x	☐	=	☐
☐	x	8	=	☐
☐	x	8	=	☐

Creepy Cave Puzzle

How many legs are there altogether in these groups of spiders?

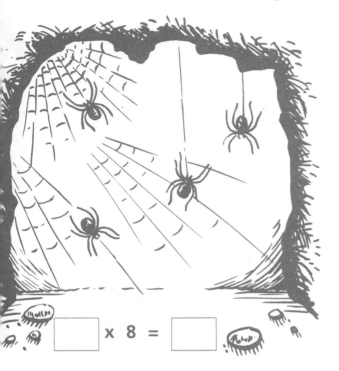

☐ x 8 = ☐

☐ x 8 = ☐

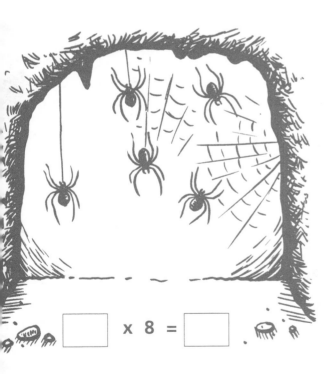

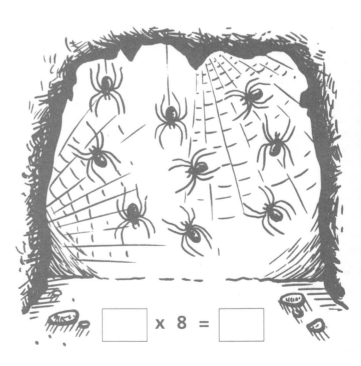

☐ x 8 = ☐

☐ x 8 = ☐

How many legs are there altogether on 11 spiders? ☐

How many legs are there altogether on 22 spiders? ☐

Record Breakers

How quickly can you do these tests?
Use a stopwatch and write the answers on spare paper.
Take 1 second off your time for every question you get **right**.
Add 3 seconds onto your time for every question you get **wrong**.

You will score better by being ACCURATE rather than FAST.

BUILD SPEED UP GRADUALLY while still trying to get all the answers right!!

Where you see ? this is the answer you need to give.

Test 1	Test 2	Test 3
1 x ? = 8	2 x ? = 8	? x 8 = 64
5 x ? = 40	3 x ? = 24	? x 7 = 49
4 x ? = 32	3 x ? = 12	? x 4 = 16
? x 8 = 24	8 x 6 = ?	? x 6 = 36
2 x 8 = ?	8 x ? = 32	? x 8 = 32
8 x 8 = ?	4 x ? = 32	? x 5 = 25
9 x 8 = ?	7 x ? = 28	? x 3 = 9
7 x 8 = ?	7 x ? = 56	? x 7 = 70
? x 8 = 96	5 x ? = 40	? x 2 = 4
10 x 8 = ?	9 x ? = 72	? x 12 = 72
? x 8 = 56	12 x ? = 96	? x 5 = 35
11 x 8 = ?	9 x ? = 54	? x 8 = 72

Keep a record of your times for each test here.

Do one test a day.

Date	Time	Date	Time	Date	Time

Times Tables

x6
x7
x8
x9
x11
x12

Key Stage 2 (England & Wales)
Mathematics 5-14 Level C (Scotland)

Book

2

ANSWERS

p3. The answers to the x6 table are: 6, 12, 18, 24, 30, 36, 42, 48, 54, 60, 66, 72.
You should mark these numbers with a O: 6, 12, 18, 24, 30, 36, 42, 48, 54, 60, 66, 72, 78, 84, 90, 96.
The shared multiples of 6 and 3 are all the multiples of 6:
6, 12, 18, 24, 30, 36, 42, 48, 54, 60, 66, 72, 78, 84, 90, 96.
The shared multiples of the x6, x3 and x2 tables are: 6, 12, 18, 24, 30, 36, 42, 48, 54, 60, 66, 72, 78, 84, 90, 96.

p4. The x6 table is 1 x 6 =6; 2 x 6 = 12; 3 x 6 = 18; 4 x 6 = 24; 5 x 6 = 30; 6 x 6 = 36;
7 x 6 = 42; 8 x 6 = 48; 9 x 6 = 54; 10 x 6 = 60; 11 x 6 = 66; 12 x 6 = 72.
The x6 table should be filled in with the numbers that are in **bold** type;
1 x **6** = 6; **2** x 6 = **12**; 3 x **6** = **18**; 4 x 6 = 24; **5** x 6 = **30**; 6 x 6 = **36**; 7 x 6 = **42**;
8 x 6 = **48**; 9 x 6 = **54**; **10** x 6 = **60**; 11 x **6** = 66; **12** x 6 = 72.

p6. The answers you need to give are:
Remember:
⬛ x 6 = 42 means what number is multiplied by 6 to give 42?
To get the answer divide 42 by 6.
42 ÷ 6 = 7

8 x ⬛ = 48 means how many lots of 8 are there in 48?
To get the answer divide 48 by 8.
48 ÷ 8 = 6

Test 1	Test 2	Test 3
7	6	5
30	6	5
2	5	5
6	5	9
6	2	8
6	6	7
6	5	4
54	6	4
4	2	3
11	4	4
72	6	9
60	6	7

p7. The answers to the x7 table are: 7, 14, 21, 28, 35, 42, 49, 56, 63, 70, 77, 84.
You should mark the following numbers on the number grid: 7, 14, 21, 28, 35, 42, 49, 56, 63, 70, 77, 84, 91, 98.

p8. The x7 table is: 1 x 7 = 7; 2 x 7 = 14; 3 x 7 = 21; 4 x 7 = 28; 5 x 7 = 35; 6 x 7 = 42;
7 x 7 = 49; 8 x 7 = 56; 9 x 7 = 63; 10 x 7 = 70; 11 x 7 = 77; 12 x 7 = 84.
The x7 table should be filled in with the numbers that are in **bold** type;
1 x **7** = 7; **2** x 7 = **14**; 3 x **7** = **21**; 4 x 7 = 28; 5 x 7 = 35; **6** x 7 = 42;
7 x 7 = **49**; 8 x 7 = 56; 9 x 7 = 63; 10 x 7 = **70**; **11** x 7 = 77; 12 x 7 = **84**

p9.

X	2	4	6	8	10
7	14	28	42	56	70
6	12	24	36	48	60
5	10	20	30	40	50

X	3	5	7	9	11
7	21	35	49	63	77
6	18	30	42	54	66
5	15	25	35	45	55

X	6	8	10	9	7
2	12	16	20	18	14
4	24	32	40	36	28
6	36	48	60	54	42

X	1	3	9	7	6
1	1	3	9	7	6
3	3	9	27	21	18
5	5	15	45	35	30

X	2	3	4	5	6
2	4	6	8	10	12
3	6	9	12	15	18
4	8	12	16	20	24
5	10	15	20	25	30
6	12	18	24	30	36

X	2	3	4	5	6	7
1	2	3	4	5	6	7
8	16	24	32	40	48	56
9	18	27	36	45	54	63
10	20	30	40	50	60	70
7	14	21	28	35	42	49
5	10	15	20	25	30	35

p10. The answers you need to give are:
Remember:
⬛ x 3 = 21 means what number is multiplied by 3 to give 21?
To get the answer divide 21 by 3.
21 ÷ 3 = 7

12 x ⬛ = 72 means how many lots of 12 are there in 72?
To get the answer divide 72 by 12.
72 ÷ 12 = 6

Test 1	Test 2	Test 3
7	7	0
7	6	6
2	7	6
7	4	9
7	6	10
49	6	9
6	7	2
7	4	4
4	2	7
7	7	11
11	6	6
84	6	7

p11. The answers to the x8 table are: 8, 16, 24, 32, 40, 48, 56, 64, 72, 80, 88, 96.
You should mark the following squares on the number grid: 8, 16, 24, 32, 40, 48, 56, 64, 72, 80, 88, 96.
The shared multiples of 8 and 4 are: 8, 16, 24, 32, 40, 48, 56, 64, 72, 80, 88, 96.
The shared multiples of 8, 4 and 2 are: 8, 16, 24, 32, 40, 48, 56, 64, 72, 80, 88, 96.

p12. The x8 table is 1 x 8 = 8;   2 x 8 = 16;   3 x 8 = 24;   4 x 8 = 32;   5 x 8 = 40;   6 x 8 = 48;
7 x 8 = 56;   8 x 8 = 64;   9 x 8 = 72;   10 x 8 = 80;   11 x 8 = 88;   12 x 8 = 96.
The x8 table should be filled in with the numbers that are in **bold** type:
1 x **8** = 8;   **2** x **8** = **16**;   3 x **8** = **24**;   4 x **8** = 32;   5 x **8** = **40**;   6 x **8** = **48**;   7 x **8** = 56;
8 x **8** = **64**;   9 x **8** = **72**;   10 x **8** = **80**;   **11** x **8** = **88**;   **12** x **8** = **96**.

p13. 4 x 8 = 32;   6 x 8 = 48;   5 x 8 = 40;   9 x 8 = 72;
11 spiders have 88 legs; 22 spiders have 176 legs;

p14. The answers you need to give are:
Remember:
⬛ x 8 = 24 means what number is multiplied by 8 to give 24?
To get the answer divide 24 by 8.
24 ÷ 8 = 3

7 x ⬛ = 56 means how many lots of 7 are there in 56?
To get the answer divide 56 by 7.
56 ÷ 7 = 8

Test 1	Test 2	Test 3
8	4	8
8	8	7
8	4	4
3	48	6
16	4	4
64	8	5
72	4	3
56	8	10
12	8	2
80	8	6
7	8	7
88	6	9

p15. The answers to the x9 table are: 9, 18, 27, 36, 45, 54, 63, 72, 81, 90, 99, 108.
You should mark the following squares
on the number grid:
9, 18, 27, 36, 45, 54, 63, 72, 81, 90, 99, 108.

> **More 9s Magic!**
> When you add the digits of each product of 9 they always add up to 9:
> 1 + 8 = 9;   2 + 7 = 9; 1 + 0 + 8 = 9.
> When you are multiplying by 9, check your answer by adding the digits together. If they add up to 9, then your answer is right.

p16. The x9 table is: 1 x 9 = 9;   2 x 9 = 18;   3 x 9 = 27;   4 x 9 = 36;   5 x 9 = 45;   6 x 9 = 54;   7 x 9 = 63;
8 x 9 = 72;   9 x 9 = 81;   10 x 9 = 90;   11 x 9 = 99;   12 x 9 = 108.
The x9 table should be filled in with the numbers that are in **bold** type:
1 x **9** = **9**;   2 x **9** = **18**;   **3** x **9** = **27**;   4 x **9** = 36;   5 x **9** = **45**;   6 x **9** = **54**;   7 x **9** = 63;
8 x **9** = **72**;   9 x **9** = 81;   **10** x **9** = **90**;   11 x **9** = **99**;   **12** x **9** = 108.

p17.

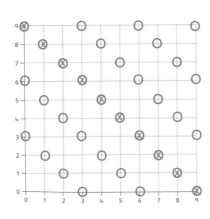

x3 table answers:
(0, 3)   (0, 6)   (0, 9)   (1, 2)   (1, 5)   (1, 8)   (2, 1)
(2, 4)   (2, 7)   (3, 0)   (3, 3)   (3, 6)   (3, 9)   (4, 2)
(4, 5)   (4, 8)   (5, 1)   (5, 4)   (5, 7)   (6, 0)   (6, 3)
(6, 6)   (6, 9)   (7, 2)   (7, 5)   (7, 8)   (8, 1)   (8, 4)
(8, 7)   (9, 0)   (9, 3)   (9, 6)   (9, 9)
The points in both sets of coordinates are:
(0, 9)   (1, 8)   (2, 7)   (3, 6)   (4, 5)   (5, 4)   (6, 3)
(7, 2)   (8, 1)   (9, 0)   (9, 9)

p18. The answers you need to give are:
Remember:
▓ x 9 = 72 means what number is multiplied by 9 to give 72?
To get the answer divide 72 by 9.
72 ÷ 9 = 8

11 x ▓ = 66 means how many lots of 11 are there in 66?
To get the answer divide 66 by 11.
66 ÷ 11 = 6

Test 1	Test 2	Test 3
9	8	3
9	6	9
4	8	6
8	8	6
27	8	4
9	7	6
11	8	5
9	9	7
72	6	6
108	3	8
9	9	12
0	9	3

p19. The answers to the x11 table are: 11, 22, 33, 44, 55, 66, 77, 88, 99, 110, 121, 132.
You should mark these squares on the number grid: 11, 22, 33, 44, 55, 66, 77, 88, 99, 110, 121, 132.

p20. The x11 table should be filled in with the numbers that are in **bold** type:
1 x **11** = 11;   **2** x 11 = 22;   **3** x 11 = **33**;   4 x **11** = **44**;   5 x **11** = **55**;   6 x 11 = **66**;   7 x **11** = 77;
8 x 11 = **88**;   9 x **11** = 99;   **10** x **11** = 110;   **11** x 11 = **121**;   12 x **11** = 132.
Quick fire answers:
Test 1: 11, 55, 66, 33, 44, 121;   **Test 2:** 36, 49, 64, 81, 144, 0.

p21. Count on in 11s to draw a time-travel machine.
Count back in 11s to draw a time-travel machine.

p22. The answers to the x12 table are: 12, 24, 36, 48, 60, 72, 84, 96, 108, 120, 132, 144.
You should mark these squares on the number grid: 12, 24, 36, 48, 60, 72, 84, 96, 108, 120, 132, 144.
The shared multiples of 12 and 6 are all the multiples of 12.
The shared multiples of 12 and 3 are all the multiples of 12.
The shared multiples of 12 and 2 are all the multiples of 12.
The shared multiples of 12 and 4 are all the multiples of 12.
The shared multiples of 12 and 8 are 24, 48, 72, 96, 120, 144.

p23. The code says:
WELL DONE! YOU ARE A TABLES CHAMP!
Give yourself a pat on the back.

p24-25.

Test 1	Test 2	Test 3	Test 4
32	12	72	5
96	8	56	9
48	84	40	4
0	35	20	10
36	24	96	7
16	96	72	8
36	72	64	12
80	28	48	3
120	70	28	2
48	108	12	1
40	88	27	11
24	0	16	10

Test 5	Test 6	Test 7	Test 8
6	8	9	7
11	2	12	5
9	5	6	10
5	7	10	2
9	12	4	9
7	6	2	9
7	11	12	8
9	12	9	11
11	5	3	1
10	10	4	0
9	11	3	12
9	3	12	1

Test 9	Test 10	Test 11	Test 12
3	3	4	7
12	5	3	2
11	4	2	6
12	9	6	2
12	5	9	2
10	2	6	2
11	4	3	4
8	2	4	6
9	8	6	8
9	9	11	3
11	12	8	4
9	9	7	8

 **table**

Write the answers to the **x9** table here.

$$1 \times 9 = \boxed{}$$

$$2 \times 9 = \boxed{}$$

$$3 \times 9 = \boxed{}$$

$$4 \times 9 = \boxed{}$$

$$5 \times 9 = \boxed{}$$

$$6 \times 9 = \boxed{}$$

$$7 \times 9 = \boxed{}$$

$$8 \times 9 = \boxed{}$$

$$9 \times 9 = \boxed{}$$

$$10 \times 9 = \boxed{}$$

$$11 \times 9 = \boxed{}$$

$$12 \times 9 = \boxed{}$$

Look at the tens and the units in the answers to the **x9** table. The units go down by one and the tens go up by one.

Mark all the answers to the **x9** table on this number grid. Use a purple **O**.

1	2	3	4	5	6	7	8	9	10
11	12	13	14	15	16	17	18	19	20
21	22	23	24	25	26	27	28	29	30
31	32	33	34	35	36	37	38	39	40
41	42	43	44	45	46	47	48	49	50
51	52	53	54	55	56	57	58	59	60
61	62	63	64	65	66	67	68	69	70
71	72	73	74	75	76	77	78	79	80
81	82	83	84	85	86	87	88	89	90
91	92	93	94	95	96	97	98	99	100
101	102	103	104	105	106	107	108	109	110

Write the **x9** table here.

☐	x	☐	=	☐	
☐	x	☐	=	☐	
☐	x	☐	=	☐	
☐	x	☐	=	☐	
☐	x	☐	=	☐	
☐	x	☐	=	☐	
☐	x	☐	=	☐	
☐	x	☐	=	☐	
☐	x	☐	=	☐	
☐	x	☐	=	☐	
☐	x	☐	=	☐	
☐	x	☐	=	☐	

Fill in the missing numbers in the **x9** table.

☐	x	9	=	9	
2	x	9	=	☐	
☐	x	9	=	☐	
☐	x	☐	=	36	
5	x	9	=	☐	
6	x	9	=	☐	
7	x	☐	=	63	
☐	x	9	=	☐	
9	x	☐	=	81	
☐	x	☐	=	90	
11	x	9	=	☐	
☐	x	☐	=	108	

Plotting Puzzles

Use the answers to the **x9** table as coordinates to complete this graph.
The first two have been done for you.

(0, 9)   (1, 8)   (2, 7)   (3, 6)   (4, 5)   (5, 4)

(6, 3)   (7, 2)   (8, 1)   (9, 0)   (9, 9)

Join the points to see what pattern you get?

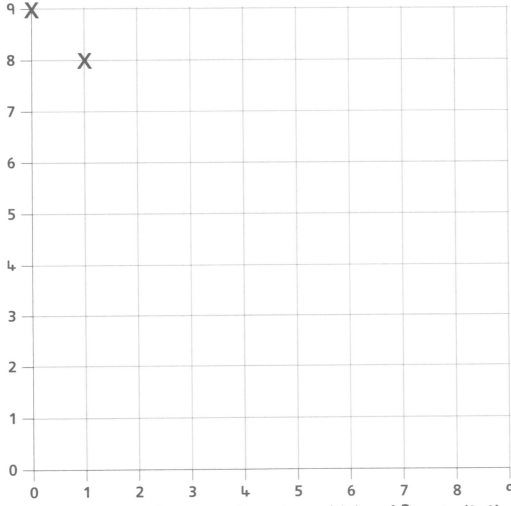

Now fill in these coordinates to show the multiples of **3** up to **(9, 9)**.

(0, 3) (0, 6) (0, 9) (1, 2) (,) (,) (,) (,)

(,) (,) (,) (,) (,) (,) (,) (,) (,)

(,) (,) (,) (,) (,) (,) (,) (,) (,)

(,) (,) (,) (,) (,) (,) (9, 9)

Mark these points on the graph. Use a different colour.
Join the points to see what pattern you get.

Which points are in both sets of coordinates?

Record Breakers

How quickly can you do these tests?
Use a stopwatch and write the answers on spare paper.
Take 1 second off your time for every question you get **right**.
Add 3 seconds onto your time for every question you get **wrong**.

You will score better by being ACCURATE rather than FAST.

BUILD SPEED UP GRADUALLY while still trying to get all the answers right!!

Where you see ? this is the answer you need to give.

Keep a record of your times for each test here.

Do one test a day.

Test 1	Test 2	Test 3
? x 9 = 81	5 x ? = 40	? x 5 = 15
? x 3 = 27	3 x ? = 18	? x 4 = 36
? x 9 = 36	6 x ? = 48	? x 2 = 12
? x 9 = 72	9 x ? = 72	? x 4 = 24
9 x 3 = ?	4 x ? = 32	? x 5 = 20
? x 6 = 54	8 x ? = 56	? x 6 = 36
? x 9 = 99	7 x ? = 56	? x 5 = 25
7 x ? = 63	2 x ? = 18	? x 7 = 49
8 x 9 = ?	11 x ? = 66	? x 7 = 42
12 x 9 = ?	9 x ? = 27	? x 9 = 72
? x 1 = 9	5 x ? = 45	? x 8 = 96
? x 9 = 0	4 x ? = 36	? x 9 = 27

Date	Time	Date	Time	Date	Time

Write the answers to the **x11** table here.

1 x 11 =		7 x 11 =
2 x 11 =		8 x 11 =
3 x 11 =		9 x 11 =
4 x 11 =		10 x 11 =
5 x 11 =		11 x 11 =
6 x 11 =		12 x 11 =

Mark all the answers to the **x11** table on this number grid.
Use a yellow **O**.

1	2	3	4	5	6	7	8	9	10
11	12	13	14	15	16	17	18	19	20
21	22	23	24	25	26	27	28	29	30
31	32	33	34	35	36	37	38	39	40
41	42	43	44	45	46	47	48	49	50
51	52	53	54	55	56	57	58	59	60
61	62	63	64	65	66	67	68	69	70
71	72	73	74	75	76	77	78	79	80
81	82	83	84	85	86	87	88	89	90
91	92	93	94	95	96	97	98	99	100
101	102	103	104	105	106	107	108	109	110
111	112	113	114	115	116	117	118	119	120
121	122	123	124	125	126	127	128	129	130
131	132	133	134	135	136	137	138	139	140

These are the **multiples of 11.**

Fill in the missing numbers in the **x11** table in the correct order.

1	x	11	=	☐
☐	x	11	=	22
☐	x	11	=	☐
4	x	☐	=	44
☐	x	11	=	☐
6	x	11	=	☐
7	x	☐	=	77
☐	x	11	=	☐
9	x	☐	=	99
☐	x	☐	=	110
☐	x	11	=	☐
☐	x	☐	=	132

Quick Fire Record Breakers

How quickly can you do these tests? Use a stopwatch and write the answers on spare paper.
Take 1 second off your time for every question you get **right.**
Add 3 seconds onto your time for every question you get **wrong.**

BUILD SPEED UP GRADUALLY while still trying to get all the answers right!!

You will score better by being ACCURATE rather than FAST.

Keep a record of your times for each test here.

Do one test a day.

Test 1		Test 2	
1 x 11 = ?		6 x 6 = ?	
5 x 11 = ?		7 x 7 = ?	
6 x 11 = ?		8 x 8 = ?	
3 x 11 = ?		9 x 9 = ?	
4 x 11 = ?		12 x 12 = ?	
11 x 11 = ?		0 x 2 = ?	
Date	Time	Date	Time

Time Travel Machines

Make your own time travel machines.

Count on in **11s** to join the dots. Start at 0.

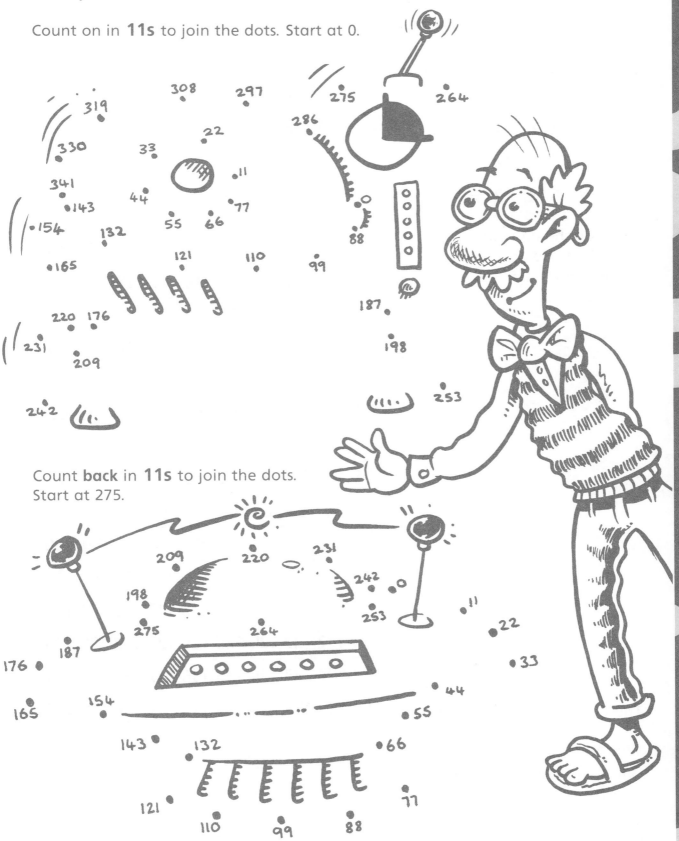

308   297   275   264

319

286

330   22

33

341   11

143   44   77

154   132   55   66

165   121   110   99   88

220   176   0

231   187

209   198

242   253

Count **back** in **11s** to join the dots.
Start at 275.

209   220   231

242

198   253   11

275   22

187   264   33

176   154   44

165   55

143   132   66

121   77

110   99   88

Write the answers to the **x12** table here.

1 x 12 = ☐		7 x 12 = ☐
2 x 12 = ☐		8 x 12 = ☐
3 x 12 = ☐		9 x 12 = ☐
4 x 12 = ☐		10 x 12 = ☐
5 x 12 = ☐		11 x 12 = ☐
6 x 12 = ☐		12 x 12 = ☐

Mark all the answers to the **x12** table on this number grid.
Use a blue **O**.

1	2	3	4	5	6	7	8	9	10
11	12	13	14	15	16	17	18	19	20
21	22	23	24	25	26	27	28	29	30
31	32	33	34	35	36	37	38	39	40
41	42	43	44	45	46	47	48	49	50
51	52	53	54	55	56	57	58	59	60
61	62	63	64	65	66	67	68	69	70
71	72	73	74	75	76	77	78	79	80
81	82	83	84	85	86	87	88	89	90
91	92	93	94	95	96	97	98	99	100
101	102	103	104	105	106	107	108	109	110
111	112	113	114	115	116	117	118	119	120
121	122	123	124	125	126	127	128	129	130
131	132	133	134	135	136	137	138	139	140
141	142	143	144	145	146	147	148	149	150

These are the **multiples of 12.**

Which multiples are also multiples of **6**? _____

Which multiples are also multiples of **3**? _____

Which multiples are also multiples of **2**? _____

Which multiples are also multiples of **4**? _____

Which multiples are also multiples of **8**? _____

Chinese Code

Use your times table facts to crack the coded message.

Here is the coded message.

8 x 11	3 x 3	8 x 4	4 x 8

2 x 4	9 x 5	10 x 4	1 x 9

!

12 x 11	5 x 9	9 x 8

1 x 2	8 x 7	3 x 3

2 x 1

7 x 10	1 x 2	4 x 1	8 x 4	3 x 3	9 x 7

3 x 2	3 x 6	1 x 2	9 x 4	10 x 5

!

More Record Breakers

Using all the times table facts in this book, how quickly can you do these tests?
Again, use a stopwatch and write the answers on spare paper.
There are more questions in each test so you'll really have to try hard.
Take 2 second off your time for every question you get **right**.
But this time **add 5 seconds onto** your time for every question you get **wrong**.

You will score better by being ACCURATE rather than FAST.

BUILD SPEED UP GRADUALLY while still trying to get all the answers right!!

Where you see ? this is the answer you need to give.

Test 1	Test 2	Test 3	Test 4
4 x 8 = ?	1 x 12 = ?	6 x 12 = ?	? x 5 = 25
8 x 12 = ?	1 x 8 = ?	7 x 8 = ?	? x 9 = 81
6 x 8 = ?	7 x 12 = ?	10 x 4 = ?	? x 4 = 16
12 x 0 = ?	7 x 5 = ?	5 x 4 = ?	? x 10 = 100
3 x 12 = ?	3 x 8 = ?	8 x 12 = ?	? x 7 = 49
2 x 8 = ?	8 x 12 = ?	9 x 8 = ?	? x 8 = 64
9 x 4 = ?	9 x 8 = ?	8 x 8 = ?	? x 12 = 144
10 x 8 = ?	7 x 4 = ?	4 x 12 = ?	? x 3 = 9
10 x 12 = ?	10 x 7 = ?	7 x 4 = ?	? x 2 = 4
4 x 12 = ?	9 x 12 = ?	3 x 4 = ?	? x 1 = 1
5 x 8 = ?	11 x 8 = ?	3 x 9 = ?	? x 11 = 121
6 x 4 = ?	0 x 12 = ?	4 x 4 = ?	? x 6 = 60

Keep a record of your times for each test here.

Do one test a day.

Date	Time	Date	Time	Date	Time	Date	Time

Test 5	Test 6	Test 7	Test 8
6 x ? = 36	? x 8 = 64	? x 2 = 18	2 x ? = 14
5 x ? = 55	2 x ? = 4	? x 5 = 60	8 x ? = 40
5 x ? = 45	? x 6 = 30	? x 10 = 60	9 x ? = 90
5 x ? = 25	6 x ? = 42	? x 2 = 20	8 x ? = 16
10 x ? = 90	? x 11 = 132	? x 5 = 20	8 x ? = 72
12 x ? = 84	11 x ? = 66	? x 10 = 20	7 x ? = 63
7 x ? = 49	? x 12 = 132	? x 2 = 24	6 x ? = 48
9 x ? = 81	12 x ? = 144	? x 5 = 45	7 x ? = 77
11 x ? = 121	? x 1 = 5	? x 10 = 30	6 x ? = 6
10 x ? = 100	12 x ? = 120	? x 2 = 8	9 x ? = 0
12 x ? = 108	? x 9 = 99	? x 5 = 15	5 x ? = 60
1 x ? = 9	3 x ? = 9	? x 10 = 120	7 x ? = 7

Date	Time	Date	Time	Date	Time	Date	Time

Keep a record of our times for each test here.

Do one test a day.

Test 9	Test 10	Test 11	Test 12
11 x ? = 33	? x 6 = 18	3 x ? = 12	? x 2 = 14
? x 5 = 60	? x 7 = 35	4 x ? = 12	? x 8 = 16
10 x ? = 110	? x 4 = 16	6 x ? = 12	? x 3 = 18
? x 3 = 36	? x 2 = 18	2 x ? = 12	? x 10 = 20
9 x ? = 108	? x 10 = 50	2 x ? = 18	? x 11 = 22
? x 2 = 20	? x 1 = 2	4 x ? = 24	? x 12 = 24
8 x ? = 88	? x 2 = 8	8 x ? = 24	? x 7 = 28
? x 10 = 80	? x 4 = 8	6 x ? = 24	? x 5 = 30
8 x ? = 72	? x 7 = 56	7 x ? = 42	? x 4 = 32
? x 4 = 36	? x 6 = 54	4 x ? = 44	? x 11 = 33
9 x ? = 99	? x 8 = 96	6 x ? = 48	? x 9 = 36
? x 3 = 27	? x 7 = 63	7 x ? = 49	? x 6 = 48

Date	Time	Date	Time	Date	Time	Date	Time

Keep a record of our times for each test here.

Do one test a day.

The Times Tables

x0 Table
```
 1 x 0 =  0
 2 x 0 =  0
 3 x 0 =  0
 4 x 0 =  0
 5 x 0 =  0
 6 x 0 =  0
 7 x 0 =  0
 8 x 0 =  0
 9 x 0 =  0
10 x 0 =  0
11 x 0 =  0
12 x 0 =  0
```

x1 Table
```
 1 x 1 =  1
 2 x 1 =  2
 3 x 1 =  3
 4 x 1 =  4
 5 x 1 =  5
 6 x 1 =  6
 7 x 1 =  7
 8 x 1 =  8
 9 x 1 =  9
10 x 1 = 10
11 x 1 = 11
12 x 1 = 12
```

x2 Table
```
 1 x 2 =  2
 2 x 2 =  4
 3 x 2 =  6
 4 x 2 =  8
 5 x 2 = 10
 6 x 2 = 12
 7 x 2 = 14
 8 x 2 = 16
 9 x 2 = 18
10 x 2 = 20
11 x 2 = 22
12 x 2 = 24
```

x3 Table
```
 1 x 3 =  3
 2 x 3 =  6
 3 x 3 =  9
 4 x 3 = 12
 5 x 3 = 15
 6 x 3 = 18
 7 x 3 = 21
 8 x 3 = 24
 9 x 3 = 27
10 x 3 = 30
11 x 3 = 33
12 x 3 = 36
```

x4 Table
```
 1 x 4 =  4
 2 x 4 =  8
 3 x 4 = 12
 4 x 4 = 16
 5 x 4 = 20
 6 x 4 = 24
 7 x 4 = 28
 8 x 4 = 32
 9 x 4 = 36
10 x 4 = 40
11 x 4 = 44
12 x 4 = 48
```

x5 Table
```
 1 x 5 =  5
 2 x 5 = 10
 3 x 5 = 15
 4 x 5 = 20
 5 x 5 = 25
 6 x 5 = 30
 7 x 5 = 35
 8 x 5 = 40
 9 x 5 = 45
10 x 5 = 50
11 x 5 = 55
12 x 5 = 60
```

x6 Table
```
 1 x 6 =  6
 2 x 6 = 12
 3 x 6 = 18
 4 x 6 = 24
 5 x 6 = 30
 6 x 6 = 36
 7 x 6 = 42
 8 x 6 = 48
 9 x 6 = 54
10 x 6 = 60
11 x 6 = 66
12 x 6 = 72
```

x7 Table
```
 1 x 7 =  7
 2 x 7 = 14
 3 x 7 = 21
 4 x 7 = 28
 5 x 7 = 35
 6 x 7 = 42
 7 x 7 = 49
 8 x 7 = 56
 9 x 7 = 63
10 x 7 = 70
11 x 7 = 77
12 x 7 = 84
```

x8 Table
```
 1 x 8 =  8      7 x 8 = 56
 2 x 8 = 16      8 x 8 = 64
 3 x 8 = 24      9 x 8 = 72
 4 x 8 = 32     10 x 8 = 80
 5 x 8 = 40     11 x 8 = 88
 6 x 8 = 48     12 x 8 = 96
```

x9 Table
```
 1 x 9 =  9      7 x 9 =  63
 2 x 9 = 18      8 x 9 =  72
 3 x 9 = 27      9 x 9 =  81
 4 x 9 = 36     10 x 9 =  90
 5 x 9 = 45     11 x 9 =  99
 6 x 9 = 54     12 x 9 = 108
```

x10 Table	x11 Table	x12 Table
1 x 10 = 10	1 x 11 = 11	1 x 12 = 12
2 x 10 = 20	2 x 11 = 22	2 x 12 = 24
3 x 10 = 30	3 x 11 = 33	3 x 12 = 36
4 x 10 = 40	4 x 11 = 44	4 x 12 = 48
5 x 10 = 50	5 x 11 = 55	5 x 12 = 60
6 x 10 = 60	6 x 11 = 66	6 x 12 = 72
7 x 10 = 70	7 x 11 = 77	7 x 12 = 84
8 x 10 = 80	8 x 11 = 88	8 x 12 = 96
9 x 10 = 90	9 x 11 = 99	9 x 12 = 108
10 x 10 = 100	10 x 11 = 110	10 x 12 = 120
11 x 10 = 110	11 x 11 = 121	11 x 12 = 132
12 x 10 = 120	12 x 11 = 132	12 x 12 = 144

You may wish to cut out or photocopy this certificate and put it up on your bedroom wall.

Certificate

This is to certify that

_____

is a

Times Tables Time Traveller

Signed_____ Date_____

Schofield&Sims

the long-established educational publisher
specialising in maths, English and science materials for schools

Times Tables is a set of books helping children to practise essential multiplication facts. Each book contains hints for learning tables, activities and time challenges, pull-out answers booklet and times tables summary.

Times Tables Book 2 (Key Stage 2) includes:
- 6 times table
- 7 times table
- 8 times table
- 9 times table
- 11 times table
- 12 times table

The full range of titles in the series is as follows:

Times Tables Book 1   ISBN 978 07217 0811 9

Times Tables Book 2   ISBN 978 07217 0812 6

Have you tried *Problem Solving* by Schofield & Sims?
This series helps children to sharpen their mathematical skills by applying their knowledge to a range of number problems and 'real-life' contexts.

For further information and to place your order
visit www.schofieldandsims.co.uk or telephone 01484 607080

ISBN 978-07217-0812-6

Schofield&Sims

Dogley Mill, Fenay Bridge, Huddersfield HD8 0NQ
Phone: 01484 607080 Facsimile: 01484 606815
E-mail: sales@schofieldandsims.co.uk
www.schofieldandsims.co.uk

ISBN 978 07217 0812 6

£2.45
(Retail price)

Key Stage 2
Age range 7–11 years

ISBN 0721708129

9 780721 708126